PUGH'S NEW YEAR'S RESOLUTIONS

Published in 2016 by
Short Books, Unit 316,
ScreenWorks, 22 Highbury Grove,
London N5 2ER

10 9 8 7 6 5 4 3 2 1

A CIP catalogue record for this book
is available from the British Library.

ISBN: 978-1-78072-288-7
Cover design and illustrations by Jonathan Pugh

Printed by CPI Group (UK) Ltd, Croydon CR0 4YY

For Kay and Paul

To Edward

So pleased to hear
you're still cartooning!
Good luck in New York!
All best wishes
Jonathan
PUGH

'You never draw beautiful people in your cartoons,' a magazine editor once said to me.

I had never given it a moment's thought. But he was absolutely right. Lustrous hair, chiselled cheekbones and granite jaws are a rarely spotted thing in my drawings, as you will gather from this collection. It's a random selection of cartoons, many of which have been published in the *Daily Mail*, and some new ones specifically drawn for this book. The theme? It's about a lot of the things we tend to think about in the New Year... food, exercise, alcohol, relationships.

My characters tend to inhabit an unfashionable world, a galaxy away from Hollywood and *Vogue*. A world of wobbly waistlines, sloping shoulders and sagging jowls, of unused gym memberships, final demands, lost car keys, cold calls and intermittent wi-fi, wine stains on the carpet and crumbs down the sofa. It's full of dog and cats, grotty weather, hippopotamuses and goldfish, garden gnomes and cups of tea, cream cakes and puddings, parking tickets and broken resolutions...

My world, in truth, and I wouldn't want it any other way.

Jonathan Pugh, 2016

" I TAKE HIM TO THE
PARK EVERY MORNING FOR
A LITTLE RUN AROUND "

"I CAN'T TELL BY YOUR EXPRESSION WHETHER YOU'RE PLEASED OR NOT..."

"BASKET!"

"THE CAT'S SCARING THE BIRDS AGAIN!!"

"OH HELLO, IT'S
YOU AGAIN "

" I'M NOT TEMPTED. I'M
TRYING TO CUT DOWN
ON SALT "

" GEORGE, THEY'VE
COME TO DRAIN
YOUR TOXINS "

"DON'T PUT YOUR HOPES
UP TOO HIGH, HAROLD "

" I KEEP GETTING
THESE URGES TO GO
OUT IN THE MIDDAY
SUN...."

"I DON'T KNOW WHERE
HE GETS THE ENERGY
FROM..... "

" I'M NOT SURE THAT'S
THE MEDITERRANEAN
DIET YOUR GP HAD
IN MIND "

"DOES MY BOTTOM LOOK BIG IN THIS?"

" THE ANNOYING THING IS
I HADN'T STOPPED .... "

"I SOMETIMES THINK ALL
WE'VE GOT IN COMMON IS
OUR BODY MASS INDEX"

"WHEN DID YOU FIRST NOTICE THIS CAT ALLERGY?"

" MARK MY WORDS -
IT WON'T LAST "

"THE BABY'S CRYING.
HIS PHONE MUST
NEED RECHARGING"

"I'VE CHANGED MY MIND. YOUR RELATIVES CAN COME HERE FOR CHRISTMAS"

" IT'S NOT A GOOD TIME.
I'LL CALL YOU BACK
WHEN THE CARRIAGE IS
FULLER "

" AH, I SEE - THE OLD THIN COP, FAT COP ROUTINE "

" JEFF, MANAGEMENT
WOULD LIKE A WORD.... "

"WE MET ONLINE AND IT
JUST BLOSSOMED INTO ONE
OF THOSE BEAUTIFUL THINGS"

" I DO WISH IT WOULD
USE THE CAT FLAP "

"I'LL BUY IT TOMORROW"

" CAN SHE CALL YOU BACK ?
SHE'S SITTING IN THE GARDEN
WAITING TO BE STUNG "

" ANNABEL, IT'S TIME
YOU KNEW — I'M NOT
A VEGETARIAN "

" I STILL THINK THE
DOG WOULD PREFER TO
GO WALKIES "

"IT'S THE SHERINGHAMS.
THEY'VE INVITED US
AROUND FOR A FASTING
EVENING "

"DO WE HAVE CREAM
FOR NECK WRINKLES?"

"WE'RE TRYING TO GET HIM TO PAY BACK SOME OF HIS VET BILL"

" WE'RE VERY COMPATIBLE. HE SLEEPS DURING THE DAY AND I SLEEP AT NIGHT "

" HAVE YOU NOTICED HOW
HE GETS FRESH FISH AND
WE GET TINS OF
PEDIGREE CHUM ? "

"I CAN SEE WHAT THEY MEAN"

" TO BE FAIR, HE WAS
HAVING SUSHI FOR LUNCH
BEFORE IT BECAME
FASHIONABLE "

" I THINK I'VE CURED
THE SNORING ..."

"ALL THIS FISH OIL
AND I CAN'T EVEN
REMEMBER MY OWN NAME"

"I DO THINK YOU OUGHT
TO HAVE A LOOK"

"DO YOU EVER WORRY
YOUR HUSBAND'S LOOKING
AT CAKES ONLINE?"

"I THINK YOU SHOULD EASE OFF THE STRAWBERRIES"

" ALL THIS TALK OF
INDEPENDENCE HAS UNSETTLED
HIM. HE NOW WANTS HIS
OWN FLAT "

" AS WE'RE HAVING THE
SAME FOOD I THOUGHT
WE MIGHT AS WELL
EAT TOGETHER "

" HE'S ENDLESSLY CHECKING
HIS PHONE AND HE HASN'T
EVEN GOT A MOBILE "

"WE'VE GOT RID OF
THE COLLAR BUT HE
STILL INSISTS ON THE TIE"

"HOW LOVELY TO SEE YOU
ENJOYING SOME 'ME' TIME"

"I'M SORRY BUT I
SPECIFICALLY ORDERED
FETA NOT CHEDDAR"

" I'LL BE HONEST, YOU'RE
NOT WHAT I WAS
EXPECTING EITHER "

"AND THEN FOR LUNCH
I HAD SOME COTTAGE
CHEESE AND A RYVITA..."

" WE CAN'T COME IN.
WE'RE ON A SUGAR
DETOX "

" THE FITBIT WAS FOR
YOU TO WEAR "

" JUST BE GRATEFUL
YOU HAVEN'T GOT
YOUR FATHER'S EARS "

"I'M JUST AS BAFFLED AS YOU ARE"

"NOTHING OF INTEREST
AS USUAL..... "

"YOU DONT EVEN
E-MAIL ME GOODNIGHT ANY
MORE ...."